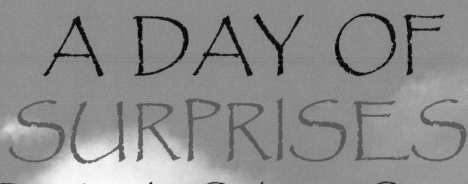

A DAY OF
SURPRISES

By Aurelie Catherine Cormier

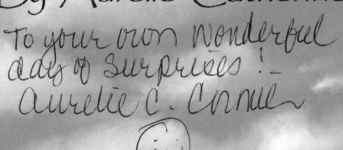

To your own wonderful
day of surprises!~
Aurelie C. Cormier
😊

A Day of Surprises by Aurelie Catherine Cormier

ISBN: 978-1-7364779-0-8 (Hardback)
ISBN: 978-1-7364779-1-5 (Paperback)
ISBN: 978-1-7364779-2-2 (Digital)

Library of Congress Control Number: 2021938979

Printed in the United States of America.

Miracle Press AND MEDIA®

Acknowledgement

I am most grateful to my Illustrator Paulo Jed for the colorful and joyful pictures that brought the story alive and to Miracle Press for their work together to bring this book from idea to children's homes! Aurelie

Did you ever have a day of surprises? Did you ever have a day with so many surprises that brought Happiness, Worry and Excitement? Matthew and Haley would soon have many surprises! Matthew was so excited. He jumped up and down, snorted and galloped off towards the barn. His sister Haley laughed and shook her head side to side and then galloped off after her brother. They both loved to pretend that they were wild horses!

Living on the farm with wide grassy pasture land, Matthew and Haley enjoyed exploring, singing and counting stars.

Today would be a day of surprises!

Taking a deep breath, Haley ran to find her mom.

Back at the house, Haley was just finishing her crunchy celery when she saw a car drive up to their farm. A lady got out of the car holding a butterscotch puppy and asked for Mrs. Griffin.

The puppy was looking straight at Haley and wagging his tail. Matthew joined in. Haley's mom took the puppy from the lady and said she would take good care of Nala.

This was their first surprise! Haley was curious. She asked her Mom, "Is this our puppy Mommy?" "This is Aunt June's puppy, Nala", Haley's mom told them, and also said that "Aunt June is sick in the hospital and we will be taking care of Nala until Aunt June gets better".

Haley and Matthew were surprised. They felt worried. They remembered when their grandpa went to the hospital and was very sick. Mrs. Griffin overheard Matthew ask Haley why she thought Aunt June was sick and what they could do to help her get better.

That night, when it was time for bedtime stories, Mr. and Mrs. Griffin both sat down with Haley and Matthew. They said that they could see that Haley and Matthew were worried and they wanted to let them know about their Aunt June. They said that sometimes people get sick just like the time they both got the flu. The doctors and nurses were doing everything possible to help her to get well and their Aunt was doing her best to get better.

Haley asked if her Mom and Dad would get sick too? Matthew asked if Nala would get sick? Her Mom said, "they were all very healthy". Haley said, "I want to do everything I can to keep Mom and Dad, Nala, Matthew and I healthy. Mr. and Mrs. Griffin said they would help Matthew and Haley learn what they could all do to stay strong and have good sunshine energy!

Mrs. Griffin said that first it was important to get a good night's sleep. She asked if they would like to take turns reading to Nala and having Nala sleep with them. Haley loved to read so she took Nala the first night. She read Nala a bedtime story. Nala listened!

The next morning Mrs. Griffin said she had an idea. She would meet Haley and Matthew in front of the garden. "This is the first thing we can do to keep healthy". They filled their baskets with deep red beets, bright red tomatoes, deep green spinach, long orange carrots and night sky blueberries. "Eat your rainbow to make your tummy smile and your body happy", said their mom!

Matthew asked, "Mom how can I eat a rainbow that is up in the sky?"

Mrs. Griffin laughed, "Matthew, let me help you with that. Eating a rainbow means to eat many colorful fruits and vegetables that are the same color as the rainbow, tomatoes are red, carrots are orange, yellow peppers are yellow, spinach is green, and blueberries are purple. Together they are the same colors as a rainbow. They help to keep your body strong."

That night, they helped their Mom by setting the table and they all nibbled on carrots, cucumbers and blueberries while waiting for dinner. They even gave small bits to Nala.

Their Mom also said it was good to drink water, especially filtered water from a glass so it was pure and clean. From now on they were going to use glass instead of plastic cups. Matthew pictured the water washing the inside of his body while he drank. Oh, he felt so good!!

The next morning, Mrs. Griffin, Haley and Matthew woke up early. They wanted to take Nala for a walk. Mrs. Griffin asked if they wanted to invite a few friends too. Haley and Matthew jumped up and down with excitement! Haley wanted to invite her best friend, Sofia. Matthew wanted to invite his best friend, Martin!

It was even more fun with their friends. Haley and Sofia were skipping and singing along the path. Matthew and Martin were bouncing, racing and exploring with Nala! They were so excited! They pretended they had magical powers that could prevent anyone or anything from getting sick!

They counted the birds... 6
And frogs... 2
They saw bunnies...   2
And a monarch butterfly...   1

What a Surprise! Their Mom told them it was a special day
to see a monarch butterfly. She winked as she told them
that they could use their magic powers to help the milkweed
to grow for the butterflies to eat! Matthew and Martin saw
themselves as Royal Princes protecting the land!!

Matthew wanted to protect Nala too. He said he had a surprise for his Mom and friends when they got home. He wanted to show them how to do Qigong that he had learned from his teacher.

First, Matthew showed them how to do jumping bean exercises to boost their energy.

Then they did balloon breathing to balance the happy energy in their bodies. Haley and Sofia put their hands over Nala to send her Love and Puppy energy. Matthew and Martin also sent healing energy to Nala and to Aunt June to help her to feel better.

That afternoon, Mrs. Griffin told Haley and Matthew she had another surprise for them. She said that Aunt June had called to say that she was starting to feel better and she would probably be coming home in a few days to live with them for a few weeks. Haley and Matthew jumped up and down and screamed with delight. Aunt June was getting better and they would see her again in a few days!! Maybe the "Qigong healing energy" had helped!!

Haley and Matthew wanted to surprise Aunt June with how well they had been taking care of Nala. They gave her a bath. They made a pretty bow to put on her collar. They took a picture together with Nala to email to Aunt June. Mrs. Griffin told Haley and Matthew how proud she was of all the loving care they were giving to Nala and sending to Aunt June.

A few days later Aunt June arrived. Haley brought Nala outdoors to see her Aunt. Aunt June was so surprised to see how big Nala was getting. Aunt June was thin but said that she felt much better. She was getting stronger everyday.

Haley asked her Aunt June if she was eating her rainbow foods, drinking clear water, taking walks and doing qigong?

Aunt June smiled and said she was trying but would love Haley to teach her more!

Aunt June said she was so proud of Haley and Matthew for watching Nala while she was in the hospital. She said their Mom had told her that they had learned how to take good care of Nala

With Rainbow Foods and Clear Water

Walks

Having fun with their friends

Practicing Qigong

Sending Good Love Energy

And Getting a Good Night's Sleep

Haley and Matthew ran towards the barn. Haley fell down in the grass and Nala jumped on her and gave her lots of wet dog kisses on her face.

Haley and Matthew giggled and looked up at the sky. They LOVED Fun Surprises! They would help to stay "Haley Strong" "Matthew Strong" and "Nala Strong" and grow healthy so they could enjoy more Fun Surprises together!

How do YOU Stay Healthy and _____ Strong

(Name)

PUT YOUR PICTURE HERE!

1. What Rainbow Foods do you eat to Stay Strong?

_____

_____

_____

_____

2. How much Water do you drink?

_____

_____

_____

_____

3. What are your Favorite Play Exercises?

_____

_____

_____

_____

4. What do you do to Feel Calm and Happy?

_____

_____

_____

_____

5. What are your Good Habits?

_____

_____

_____

_____

6. Who are your Best Friends?

_____

_____

_____

_____

7. What other things do you do to Stay Strong and Healthy?

_____

_____

_____

_____

Upside Down Suggestions to help YOU to Stay Healthy and Strong:

1. Food: Eat your rainbow foods: organic or natural fresh fruits and veggies, beans, grains, legumes, nuts (if possible) and good oils like olive oil and avocado.

2. Water: Drink clear filtered water from a glass or steel lined container

3. Play and Exercise: Move, get fresh air and exercise much of the day. Do something Fun that you Love! Walk, run, play, do jungle gyms, swimming, biking, exploring.

4. Feeling Calm and Happy: take a deep breath. Do kids qigong, kids' yoga or meditation for 5-10 minutes a day with your Mom, Dad, Teacher or Friend. When you are feeling scared or worried, take a pause-put your hands on your heart and belly and take a slow deep belly breath in and out. Let your Mom and Dad know how you feel!

5. Good Habits: Wash your hands, brush your teeth, leave your shoes and sneakers at the door, wear slippers, socks or go barefoot in the house. Ask your Mom or Dad to avoid chemicals in the house or on the lawn. Have a tub bath every night, Sleep and Dream!

6. Friends: Have play time with your friends. Share. Say Please and Thank you. Be Kind, Be Helpful, Be understanding, do something with your friends along with your Mom or Dad to Help Others. Have Fun and Be You!

7. Other things you might do to stay Strong and Healthy: Laugh. Visit a Farm, plant some Seeds, Draw a Picture, have your Mom or Dad help you to Write your own Book!

This book is dedicated to my daughter Kelsey Elizabeth Warren Mullikin. God Blessed me the Day I became your Mom and you have been a wonderful teacher for my Soul!!

It is also dedicated to all the Youth in this world who inspire and teach us each day with their Authentic Creativity, Wonder, Awe, and Curiosity for all of Life!

The writing of this book was inspired by my cousin, Kathleen McCarthy Sullivan, who survived Hodgkin's disease in 1969 and Lived Life with Humor and Creativity! She encouraged me to write this book to inspire young children to delight in the habits of healthy living!

Aurelie Catherine Cormier RN MS ANP-BC is the Founder and CEO of Aurelie Cormier's W.E.L.L.N.E.S.S.© Parenting. She has always had a Passion for Prevention, and after working with many of her patients with Cancer, for Survivorship and Healing too. She grew up on Cape Cod where, as a toddler, she witnessed and helped her Uncle Jack recover from open heart surgery done in 1958 at Boston Children's Hospital. It took a year for him to recover and in the process her family was transformed by living a Healthy Heart Lifestyle. It became as natural as breathing. She loves to run, has a passion for healthy eating, visiting historic places and traveling to sacred spaces. She considers the time spent helping to raise her daughter as her proudest accomplishment. You can learn more by going to www.bWellnessParenting.com